I've Been Working on the Railroad

I've Been Working on the Railroad

Nadine Bernard Westcott

A TRUMPET CLUB SPECIAL EDITION

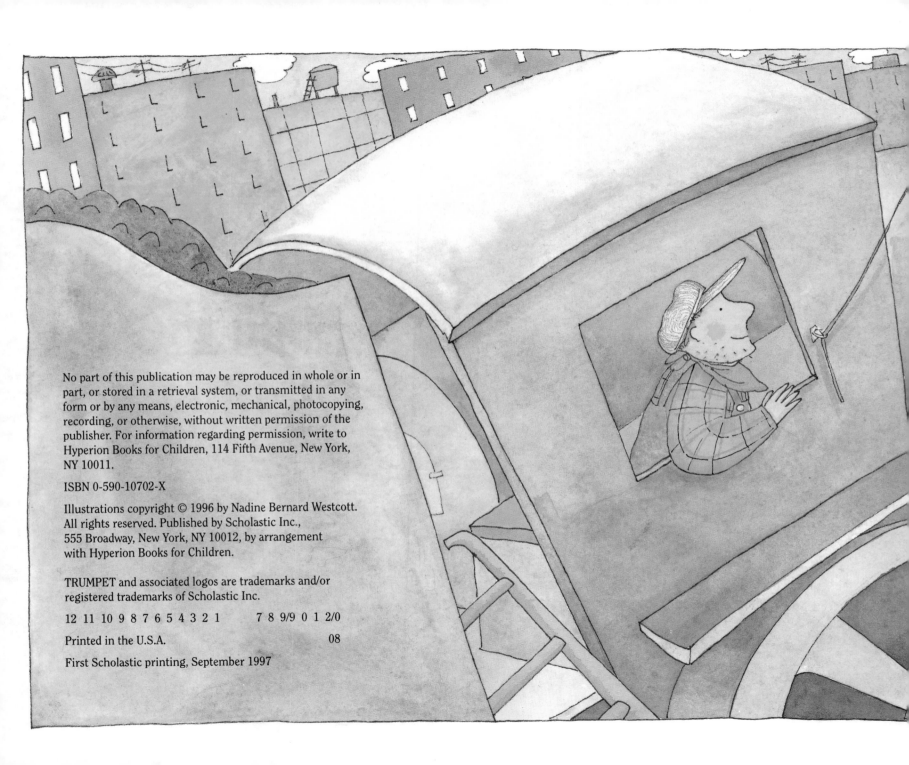

ISBN 0-590-10702-X

Illustrations copyright © 1996 by Nadine Bernard Westcott. All rights reserved. Published by Scholastic Inc., 555 Broadway, New York, NY 10012, by arrangement with Hyperion Books for Children.

TRUMPET and associated logos are trademarks and/or registered trademarks of Scholastic Inc.

12 11 10 9 8 7 6 5 4 3 2 1   7 8 9/9 0 1 2/0

Printed in the U.S.A.   08

First Scholastic printing, September 1997

For Willy

I've been working on
the railroad

All the livelong day.

I've been working on
the railroad

Just to pass the time away.

Can't you hear
the whistle blowing?

Rise up so early in the morn.

Can't you hear
the captain shouting,
Dinah, blow your horn!

Dinah, won't you blow,
Dinah, won't you blow,
Dinah, won't you blow your
horn, horn, horn?
Dinah, won't you blow,
Dinah, won't you blow,
Dinah, won't you blow
your horn?

Someone's in the kitchen
with Dinah.
Someone's in the kitchen
I know-o-o-o.
Someone's in the kitchen
with Dinah,
Strummin' on the old banjo . . .

And singing, *Fee-fi-fiddlee-i-o,*
Fee-fi-fiddlee-i-o-o-o-o,

Fee-fi-fiddlee-i-o,

Strummin' on the old banjo.

I've Been Working on the Railroad

The origins of "I've Been Working on the Railroad" are uncertain. It is thought to be modified from a levee tune sung by black railroad workers in the late nineteenth century. Little is known about its oral tradition, although it may have been based on older work songs of riverboating days.

The earliest known date for the song's publication is 1894, in the eighth edition of *Carmina Princetonia*, a college songbook. The song's omission from the previous edition supports the idea that it was not widely popular prior to the early 1890s.

The song grew in popularity in the twentieth century—especially among barbershop quartets in the early 1900s—until by midcentury it was a facet of camp life for American children in all fifty states. And it remains so!